PLANTS VS. ZOMBIES

GARDEN WARFARE

VOLUME 3

Written by PAUL TOBIN
Art by JACOB CHABOT
Colors by HEATHER BRECKEL
Letters by STEVE DUTRO
Cover by JACOB CHABOT

DARK HORSE BOOKS

Publisher MIKE RICHARDSON
Senior Editor PHILIP R. SIMON
Associate Editor MEGAN WALKER
Assistant Editor JOSHUA ENGLEDOW
Designer BRENNAN THOME
Digital Art Technician CHRISTIANNE GILLENARDO-GOUDREAU

Special thanks to A.J. Rathbun, Kristen Star, Kevin Lee, Amanda Doiron,
Justin Wiebe, Kyle Duncan. Rachel Downing, Emerson Oaks,
Mario Sanchez, and everyone at PopCap Games and EA Games.

First Edition: November 2019
ISBN 978-1-50670-837-9
Digital ISBN 978-1-50670-580-4

10 9 8 7 6 5 4 3 2 1
Printed in China

DarkHorse.com | PopCap.com

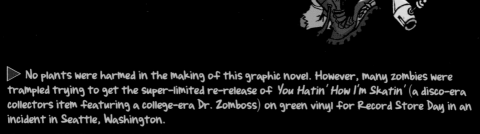

▷ No plants were harmed in the making of this graphic novel. However, many zombies were trampled trying to get the super-limited re-release of *You Hatin' How I'm Skatin'* (a disco-era collectors item featuring a college-era Dr. Zomboss) on green vinyl for Record Store Day in an incident in Seattle, Washington.

PLANTS vs. ZOMBIES: GARDEN WARFARE VOLUME 3 | Published by Dark Horse Books, a division of Dark Horse Comics, LLC, 10956 SE Main Street, Milwaukie, OR 97222 | To find a comics shop in your area, visit comicshoplocator.com |

Library of Congress Cataloging-in-Publication Data

Names: Tobin, Paul, writer. | Chabot, Jacob, artist. | Breckel, Heather,
    colourist. | Dutro, Steve, letterer.
Title: Plants vs. zombies. Garden warfare volume 3 / written by Paul Tobin
    ; art by Jacob Chabot ; colors by Heather Breckel ; letters by Steve
    Dutro ; cover by Jacob Chabot.
Other titles: Plants versus zombies. Garden warfare
Description: First edition. | Milwaukie, OR : Dark Horse Books, 2019. |
    Audience: Ages 8+ | Audience: Grades 2-3 | Summary: "When Zomboss
    creates kid robots to mimic Nate and Patrice and lead the plants astray,
    Crazy Dave unleashes some new inventions-and introduces some surprising
    additions to the Neighborville team!"-- Provided by publisher.
Identifiers: LCCN 2019023647 (print) | LCCN 2019023648 (ebook) | ISBN
    9781506708379 (hardcover) | ISBN 9781506705804 (ebook)
Subjects: LCSH: Graphic novels. | CYAC: Graphic novels. | Science fiction.
    | Plants--Fiction. | Zombies--Fiction.
Classification: LCC PZ7.7.T62 Pie 2019 (print) | LCC PZ7.7.T62 (ebook) |
    DDC 741.5/973--dc23
LC record available at https://lccn.loc.gov/2019023647
LC ebook record available at https://lccn.loc.gov/2019023648

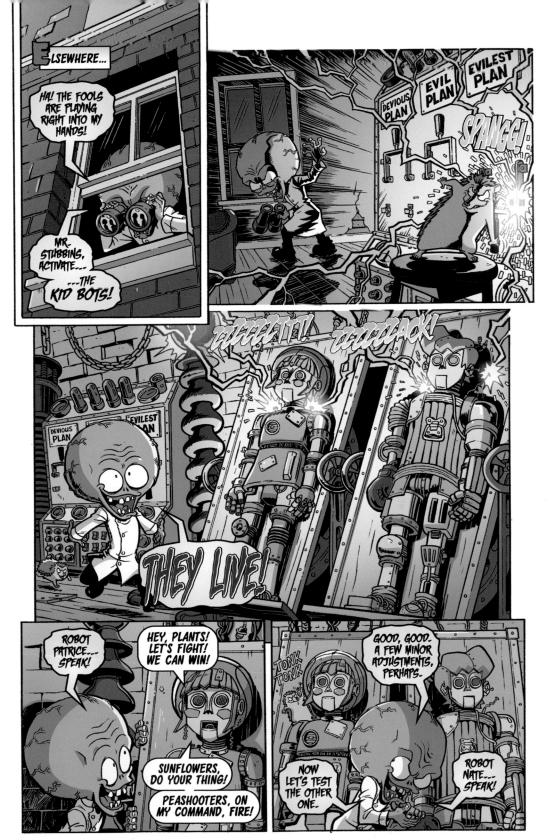

9

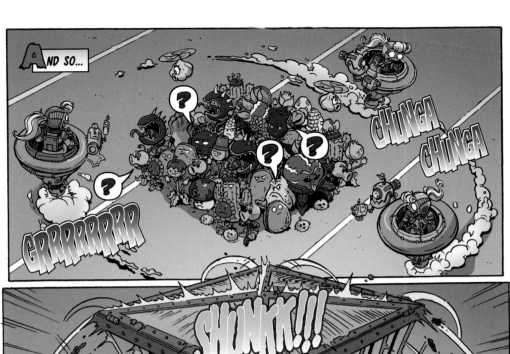

AND SO...

SHUNKK!!!

HA HA HA! YOU WITLESS PLANTS FELL FOR MY GENIUS RUSE, FOLLOWING MERE ROBOTS TO THIS STADIUM, AND NOW...

WAGGLE

WAGGLE

...MY TRAP IS COMPLETE!

22

OUR CURRENT PROBLEM IS, EVEN THE "SAUSAGE" DESTINATIONS ARE IN ZOMBIE-OCCUPIED TERRITORY.

IN FACT, PRETTY MUCH ALL AREAS ARE ZOMBIE-OCCUPIED TERRITORY.

"WE'LL HAVE TO BE VERY CAREFUL OF THE ZOMBIE PATROLS, EVEN IF THEY AREN'T PARTICULARLY OBSERVANT."

HIDING

BECAUSE THE ONLY PLANTS THAT *WEREN'T* TRAPPED IN THE STADIUM ARE THESE SUNFLOWERS.

THEY JUST HAPPENED TO BE ON AN ICE CREAM BREAK WHEN ZOMBOSS STRUCK.

OH, NO! WHAT A TRAGEDY!

RIGHT? ALL THOSE OTHER PLANTS! TRAPPED!

OH, YEAH. I ACTUALLY MEANT THAT IT WAS TRAGIC THAT THE SUNFLOWERS DIDN'T BRING ME ANY ICE CREAM.

BUT... YES!...THAT OTHER THING, TOO!

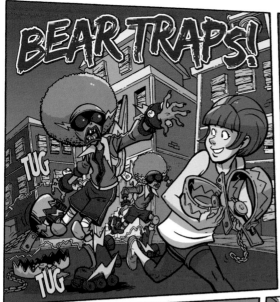

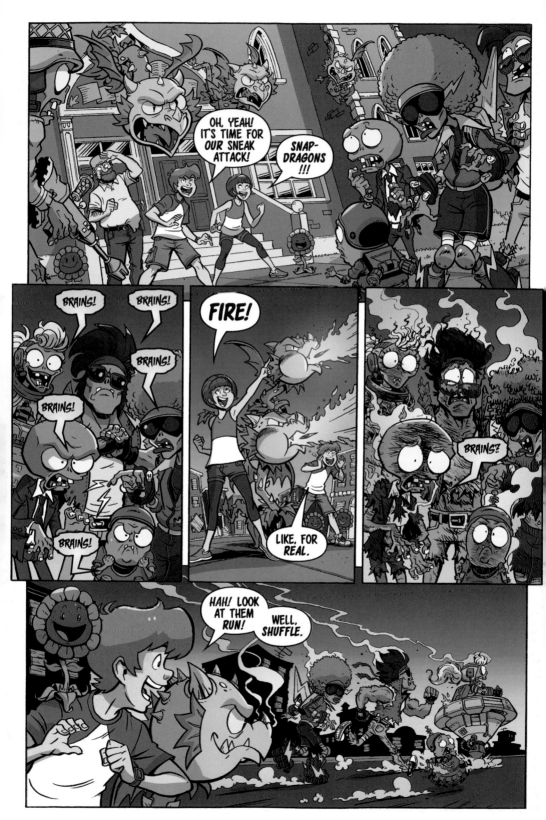

OKAY, YOU'RE WEIRD, BUT...THIS MUSIC, THIS DARKNESS, IT'S EVEN MORE STRANGE.

"EVEN THE ZOMBIES ARE FREAKING OUT!"

BRAINS?

"WAIT, I THINK MAYBE... I SEE SOMETHING?"

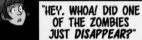

"HEY, WHOA! DID ONE OF THE ZOMBIES JUST DISAPPEAR?"

BRAINS?

BRAINS?

"ANOTHER ONE! SOMETHING IS GRABBING THEM INTO THE DARKNESS! AND INTO THE MIST!"

BRAINS?

UH, THE MIST IS ME AGAIN. I NEEDED TO WASH MY FEET.

NOT SURE HOW, BUT I GOT MARSH-MALLOWS INSIDE MY SHOES.

FWSSSS

HMM, I THINK... I THINK THE DARKNESS IS CLEARING.

WHOA! LOOK AT THIS!

HERE'S MORE OF THEM.

HOLD ON! SOMETHING'S COMING FROM THE DARK-NESS!

IT'S... IT'S...

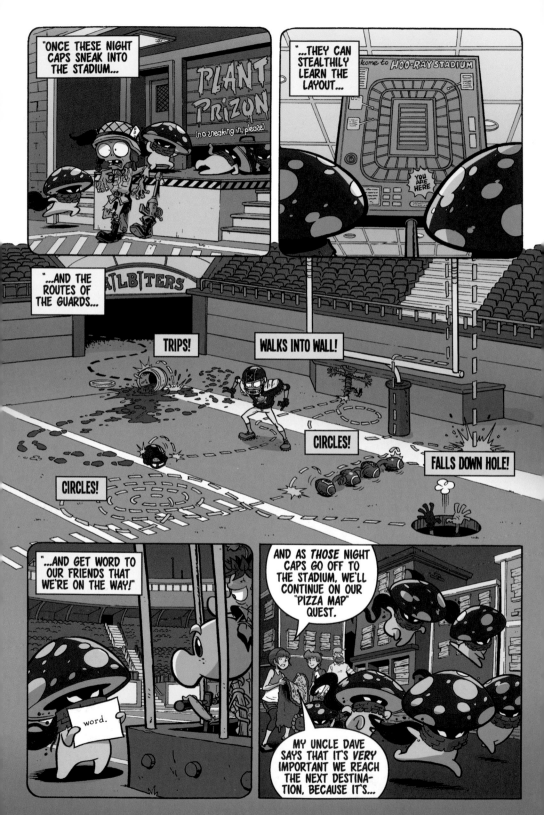

...AN ARTIST'S RECEPTION AT A GALLERY SHOWCASING RARE EXAMPLES OF CELEBRITY TAFFY.

HMMM.

UNCLE DAVE, I'M NOT SURE THIS IS *ALL THAT IMPORTANT* IN AN ONGOING WAR AGAINST ZOMBIES.

YOU'RE *WRONG*, PATRICE. YOU NEED TO LOOK AT THE *BIG PICTURE!* FIRST...

"...CRAZY DAVE JUST FOUND THE TAFFY FOR TWO TEETH TINA, COMPLETING HIS COLLECTION OF UNSETTLING CIRCUS CLOWNS. SECONDLY...AND THIS IS FAR MORE IMPORTANT..."

...THERE'S FREE ICE CREAM!

44

OKAY, WE HAVE TO BE SNEAKY, AND AS QUIET AS POSSIBLE, SO EVERYONE...

...FOLLOW THE NIGHT CAPS' LEAD.

AND PLEASE, NOBODY FOLLOW *NATE'S* LEAD.

MUNCH MUNCH CRUNCH MUNCH

"FROM WHAT THE NIGHT CAPS HAVE TOLD US, ALL OF THE PLANTS ARE BEING HELD IN A GIANT CAGE IN THE MIDDLE OF THE FIELD. BUT...IT DOESN'T HAVE A TOP TO IT. MAYBE WE CAN GET THEM OUT THAT WAY?"

BUT...WHY ARE THE NIGHT CAPS SHOWING US THIS HUGE INFLATABLE DISCO BALL?

IT'S JUST A PROP FOR WHEN OUR DIAMOND DOGS DISCO TEAM PLAYS.

HMMM.

OKAY! I GOT IT! SNAPDRAGONS! I NEED YOU TO BLOW IN HERE!

WE'RE GOING TO INFLATE THIS LIKE A BALLOON!

FLOAT

FLOAT

IN SPECIFIC, LIKE A HOT AIR BALLOON!

FLOAT

EVERYONE GET ON!

HA! WE CAN RIDE THIS BALLOON UP AND OUT OF THE STADIUM!

HANG ON, EVERYONE!

CAN WE STOP OFF AT A PIZZA PLACE? RESCUE MISSIONS MAKE ME HUNGRY.

BRAINS?

BRAAAINZ?

WE MADE IT, EVERYONE!

YOU'RE FREE!!!

WELCOME TO THE HOME OF THE NEIGHBORVILLE NAILBITERS!

WITH ALL OF US TOGETHER NOW, THIS FIGHT'S GOING TO BE EASY!

AHH! WHAT TO DO? WHAT TO DO?

HMMM.

GRAB!

TIE!

THERE! NOW IT'S SERIOUS!

ESCAPE!

PIN!

YOU GOT HIM!

I CAN'T BELIEVE YOU WERE STRONG ENOUGH!

WELL, THANKS, BUT MOSTLY I THINK...

"...IT WAS ALL THE STICKY MARSHMALLOW GOOP I HAD ON MY HANDS THAT SUPER-GLUED HIS THUMB DOWN.

TREMBLE TREMBLE

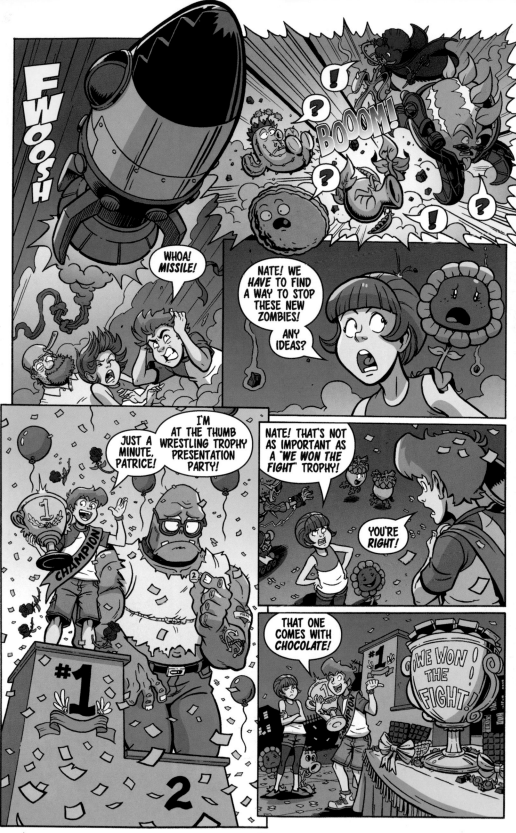

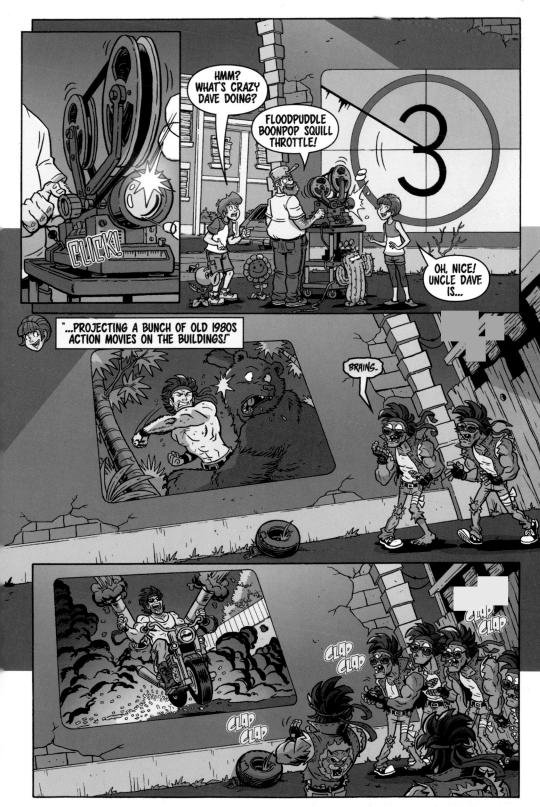

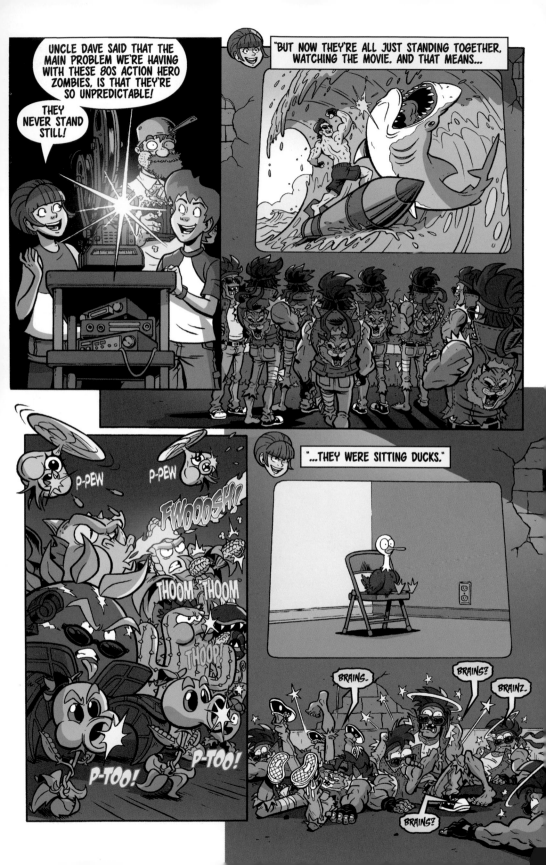

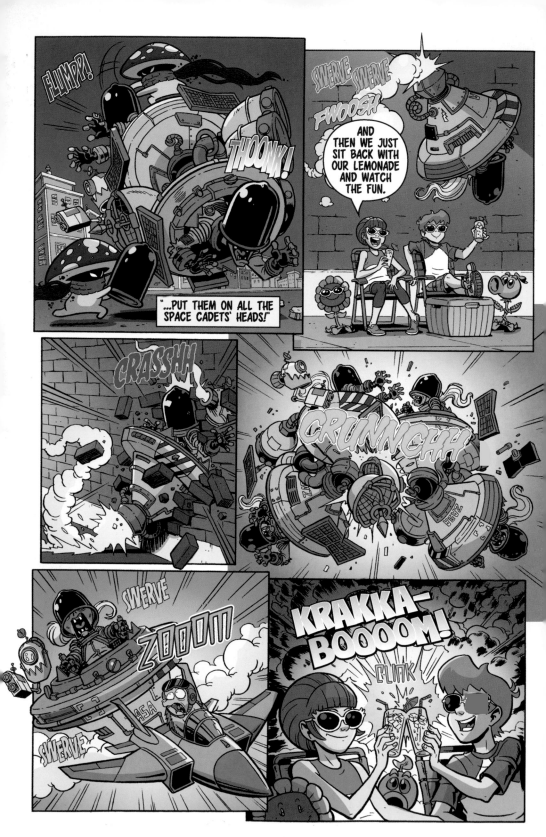

STEBBLE FLOUNDRY FLOP.

WHY'S CRAZY DAVE LOOK SO SAD?

OH, IT'S BECAUSE OF...

"...THE ELECTRIC SLIDES.

"UNCLE DAVE SAYS THAT WE CAN'T KEEP UP WITH THEM ON THEIR SKATES, ESPECIALLY WITH THEIR ODD MOVEMENTS MAKING THEM ENTIRELY UNPREDICTABLE, SO IN ORDER TO STOP THEM, HE'S GOING TO HAVE TO SACRIFICE ALL OF...

...HIS CELEBRITY TAFFY.

COME ON, NATE! PUT ALL THE TAFFY HERE IN THIS BIG IRON POT!

chuzza chuzza chuzza

Big Pat's Big Pots

AND NOW WE GET THE SNAPDRAGONS TO HEAT IT UP!

ROOAAR FWOOSH

I REALLY HAVE TO STOP MAKING THESE PREDICTIONS.

AND SO...

AFTER THEM, MY ZOMBIES!

RUN RUN   RUN RUN

SHUFFLE SHUFFLE

RUN RUN

SKATE SKATE   SHUFFLE

THERE! THEY'RE GOING INTO THAT ALLEY!

"WE'VE MANAGED TO SEPARATE THEM FROM THE PLANTS! THEY'RE HELPLESS!"

SHUFFLE

SHUFFLE

SKATE SKATE

JOG JOG

KINDA-RUN

AFTER THEM! THEY WENT INTO---

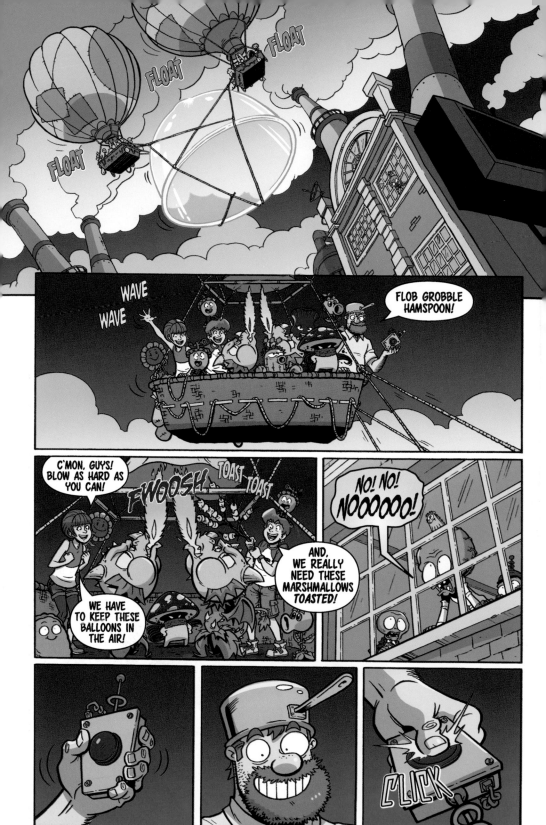

AND, SOON...

IT'S SO *NICE* TO SAFELY WALK THE STREETS OF NEIGHBORVILLE AGAIN!

ELSEWHERE...

"NOW THAT UNCLE DAVE TRAPPED ZOMBOSS' HEADQUARTERS UNDER THAT GIANT GLASS TERRARIUM..."

"...THERE ARE NO MORE ZOMBIES LEFT TO WORRY ABOUT!"

"I GUESS WE WON'T HAVE TO TRACK DOWN THOSE INVASIVE PLANTS AFTER ALL."

"STILL, THOUGH..."

TAP TAP TAP

"...I KIND OF WONDER WHAT THEY'RE LIKE."

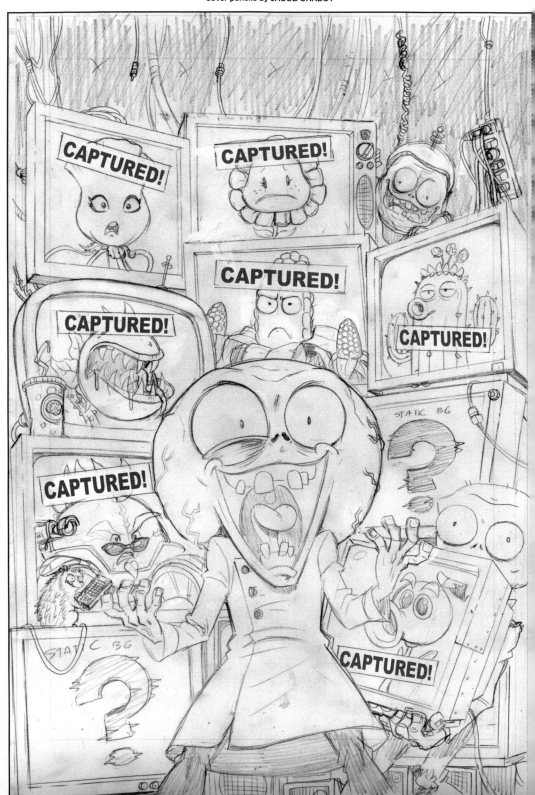

CREATOR BIOS

Paul Tobin

Jacob Chabot

PAUL TOBIN enjoys that his author photo makes him look insane, and he once accidentally cut his ear with a potato chip. He doesn't know how it happened, either. Life is so full of mystery. If you ask him about the Potato Chip Incident, he'll just make up a story. That's what he does. He's written hundreds of stories for Marvel, DC, Dark Horse, and many others, including such creator-owned titles as *Colder* and *Bandette*, as well as *Prepare to Die!*—his debut novel. His *Genius Factor* series of novels about a fifth-grade genius and his war against the Red Death Tea Society debuted in March 2016 with *How to Capture an Invisible Cat*, from Bloomsbury Publishing, and continued in early 2017 with *How to Outsmart a Billion Robot Bees*. Paul has won some Very Important Awards for his writing but so far none for his karaoke skills.

JACOB CHABOT is a New York City-based cartoonist and illustrator. His credits include work for *SpongeBob Comics*, *Simpsons Comics*, *Marvel Super Hero Adventures*, *Hello Kitty*, and his own Eisner nominated book *The Mighty Skullboy Army* (published by Dark Horse Comics). Jacob has already drawn three *Plants vs. Zombies* graphic novels that you may have read: *Garden Warfare Volume 1*, *Boom Boom Mushroom*, and *The Greatest Show Unearthed*! He also has almost all the achievements in *Plants vs. Zombies Garden Warfare* and *Garden Warfare 2* now, and if he could stop drawing for a minute, maybe he could finish them all!

Heather Breckel

Steve Dutro

HEATHER BRECKEL went to the Columbus College of Art and Design for animation. She decided animation wasn't for her so she switched to comics. She's been working as a colorist for nearly ten years and has worked for nearly every major comics publisher out there. When she's not burning the midnight oil in a deadline crunch, she's either dying a bunch in videogames or telling her cats to stop running around at two in the morning.

STEVE DUTRO is an Eisner Award–nominated comic-book letterer from Redding, California, who can also drive a tractor. He graduated from the Kubert School and has been lettering comics since the days when foil-embossed covers were cool, working for Dark Horse (*The Fifth Beatle*, *I Am a Hero*, *Planet of the Apes*, *Star Wars*), Viz, Marvel, and DC. He has submitted a request to the Department of Homeland Security that in the event of a zombie apocalypse he be put in charge of all digital freeway signs so citizens can be alerted to avoid nearby brain-eatings and the like. He finds the *Plants vs. Zombies* game to be a real stress-fest, but highly recommends the *Plants vs. Zombies* table on *Pinball FX2* for game-room hipsters.

ALSO AVAILABLE FROM DARK HORSE!

THE HIT VIDEO GAME CONTINUES ITS COMIC BOOK INVASION!

PLANTS VS. ZOMBIES: LAWNMAGEDDON
Crazy Dave—the babbling-yet-brilliant inventor and top-notch neighborhood defender—helps young adventurer Nate fend off a zombie invasion that threatens to overrun the peaceful town of Neighborville in *Plants vs. Zombies: Lawnmageddon*! Their only hope is a brave army of chomping, squashing, and pea-shooting plants! A wacky adventure for zombie zappers young and old!
ISBN 978-1-61655-192-6 | $9.99

THE ART OF PLANTS VS. ZOMBIES
Part zombie memoir, part celebration of zombie triumphs, and part anti-plant screed, *The Art of Plants vs. Zombies* is a treasure trove of never-before-seen concept art, character sketches, and surprises from PopCap's popular *Plants vs. Zombies* games!
ISBN 978-1-61655-331-9 | $9.99

PLANTS VS. ZOMBIES: TIMEPOCALYPSE
Crazy Dave helps Patrice and Nate Timely fend off Zomboss' latest attack in *Plants vs. Zombies: Timepocalypse*! This new standalone tale will tickle your funny bones and thrill your brains through any timeline!
ISBN 978-1-61655-621-1 | $9.99

PLANTS VS. ZOMBIES: BULLY FOR YOU
Patrice and Nate are ready to investigate a strange college campus to keep the streets safe from zombies!
ISBN 978-1-61655-889-5 | $9.99

PLANTS VS. ZOMBIES: GARDEN WARFARE VOLUME 1
Based on the hit video game, this comic tells the story leading up to the events in *Plants vs. Zombies: Garden Warfare 2*!
ISBN 978-1-61655-946-5 | $9.99

VOLUME 2
ISBN 978-1-50670-548-4 | $9.99

PLANTS VS. ZOMBIES: GROWN SWEET HOME
With newfound knowledge of humanity, Dr. Zomboss strikes at the heart of Neighborville . . . sparking a series of plant-versus-zombie brawls!
ISBN 978-1-61655-971-7 | $9.99

PLANTS VS. ZOMBIES: PETAL TO THE METAL
Crazy Dave takes on the tough *Don't Blink* video game—and challenges Dr. Zomboss to a race to determine the future of Neighborville!
ISBN 978-1-61655-999-1 | $9.99

PLANTS VS. ZOMBIES: BOOM BOOM MUSHROOM
The gang discover Zomboss' secret plan for swallowing the city of Neighborville whole! A rare mushroom must be found in order to save the humans aboveground!
ISBN 978-1-50670-037-3 | $9.99

PLANTS VS. ZOMBIES: BATTLE EXTRAVAGONZO
Zomboss is back, hoping to buy the same factory that Crazy Dave is eyeing! Will Crazy Dave and his intelligent plants beat Zomboss and his zombie army to the punch?
ISBN 978-1-50670-189-9 | $9.99

PLANTS VS. ZOMBIES: LAWN OF DOOM
With Zomboss filling everyone's yards with traps and special soldiers, will he and his zombie army turn Halloween into their zanier Lawn of Doom celebration?!
ISBN 978-1-50670-204-9 | $9.99

PLANTS VS. ZOMBIES: THE GREATEST SHOW UNEARTHED
Dr. Zomboss believes that all humans hold a secret desire to run away and join the circus, so he aims to use his "Big Z's Adequately Amazing Flytrap Circus" to lure Neighborville's citizens to their doom!
ISBN 978-1-50670-298-8 | $9.99

PLANTS VS. ZOMBIES: RUMBLE AT LAKE GUMBO
The battle for clean water begins! Nate, Patrice, and Crazy Dave spot trouble and grab all the Tangle Kelp and Party Crabs they can to quell another zombie attack!
ISBN 978 1-50670-497-5 | $9.99

PLANTS VS. ZOMBIES: WAR AND PEAS
When Dr. Zomboss and Crazy Dave find themselves members of the same book club, a literary war is inevitable! The position of leader of the book club opens up and Zomboss and Crazy Dave compete for the top spot in a scholarly scuffle for the ages!
ISBN 978-1-50670-677-1 | $9.99

PLANTS VS. ZOMBIES: DINO-MIGHT
Dr. Zomboss sets his sights on destroying the yards in town and rendering the plants homeless—and his plans include dogs, cats, rabbits, hammock sloths, and, somehow, dinosaurs . . . !
ISBN 978-1-50670-838-6 | $9.99

PLANTS VS. ZOMBIES: SNOW THANKS
Dr. Zomboss invents a Cold Crystal capable of freezing Neighborville, burying the town in snow and ice! It's up to the humans and the fieriest plants to save Neighborville—with the help of pirates!
ISBN 978-1-50670-839-3 | $9.99

PLANTS VS. ZOMBIES: A LITTLE PROBLEM
Will an invasion of teeny-tiny miniature zombies mean the party for Crazy Dave's two-hundred-year-old pants gets canceled?
ISBN 978-1-50670-840-9 | $9.99